Whacky Jack! ™

Written by Jonathan London
Illustrated by Doug Cushman

For my dad, 1915–1995
—J.L.

Hooked On Phonics ®

"Jack!" says Dad.
"Let's play catch!"

Jack grabs his new mitt.
He smacks it. He whacks it.
Then he runs out back with Dad.

"Catch!" says Dad.

Up, up, up zips the ball.
Down, down, down, it drops...

smack on Jack's nose! BUMP!
"Oh!" says Jack.
"That hit my nose!"

"Oh, no!" says Dad
and hugs Jack.
"Let's get the bat!"

Jack grabs his bat,
and Dad pitches the ball.
"Swing!" says Dad.

Jack hits the ball! CRACK!
Up, up, up zips the ball.

Down, down, down it drops...
smack on Jack's nose. BUMP!
"Oh!" says Jack and rubs
his nose.

"Oh, no!" says Dad and
pats Jack.
    Dad and Jack go back.

Jack drinks a glass of milk.
He sits and rubs his nose.

Then Jack has a bath...

and gets into bed.

"I can't catch, and I can't hit!"
says Jack.

"Do not sulk," says Dad.
"If you work at it, you can
be a champ!"

When the sun comes up
Jack gets out of bed. He grabs
his mitt. He smacks it.
He whacks it.

He gets his bat. He swings it!

At sunset Jack and Dad
run to the park.
"Play ball!" says Dad.
Jack jogs out to the grass.

He checks his hat.

He socks his mitt.

"Catch!" says Dad.
Up, up, up, zips the ball.

Down, down, down it drops...
smack into Jack's mitt!
"Good catch!" says Dad.

Then Dad says, "Batter up!"
Dad pitches the ball to Jack.

Jack swings his bat...

and hits the ball! CRACK!
He slams it! He smacks it!
He whacks it!

Up, up, up, zips the ball.
Down, down, down, it drops...
smack on Dad's head! THUD!

"Oh!" Dad says
and rubs his head.
"Oh, no!" says Jack.
He hugs Dad.

"See, when you work at it,
you can be a champ," says Dad.
"You whacked that ball!"

"From now on I will call you

WHACKY JACK!"